pocket: *adjective:* small enough
issue: *noun:* a vital or unsettled

Born from a frustration with today's sound-bite
news, Pocket Issue titles pull together the background to some of
the biggest challenges facing our world – delivering the facts in an
independent and quick-to-digest format.

Designed for our time-pressed lives, these short and pithy
handbooks quickly brief you with enough facts to join the debate.

Praise for Pocket Issue:

*'A brilliant wheeze: The essence of the debate in a very
approachable format.'* Harriet Lane, The Observer

*'Exactly what any busy person needs – the facts at your fingertips!
Never get caught out again when a conversation starts on the big
issues of our time.'* Jeremy Vine, BBC Radio 2 and Panorama

*'For everyone who longs to be well-informed but lacks the time
(or attention span).'* Alex Clark, The Observer

*'Prep yourself by keeping the one on global warming in the
downstairs loo...'* Mary Killen, The Spectator

'Precisely what's needed...' Hephzibah Anderson, The Daily Mail

Dig deeper on any issue we cover through our blog, plus get news
of new publications and special offers on our website,
www.**pocket***issue*.com. And tell us what you think, we always
welcome your suggestions and comments.

Now available in Audio – Order online at
www.**pocket***issue*.com

Pocket issue
Small briefs for a big world

Pocket Issue
Pandemics

Bird flu, MRSA –
Should we be worried?

Published by Pocket Issue, London
www.**pocket***issue*.com
info@**pocket***issue*.com

Copyright © Pocket Issue, 2008

ISBN: 978-0-9554415-4-7
ISBN: 0-9554415-4-4

The contents of this publication are believed to be correct at the
time of printing. Nevertheless, the publisher can accept no
responsibility for errors or omissions, changes in the details given,
or for any expense or loss thereby caused.

Design and production by Sanchez Design.
www.sanchezdesign.co.uk

Pocket
ISSUE

Each Pocket Issue is written to a standard editorial template. For *Pandemics: Bird flu, MRSA – Should we be worried?* we would like to thank the following team:

Researcher: Waseem Yaqoob
Author: Mary Alexander
Illustrations: Andrzej Krauze
Design: Daniel Sanchez
Editorial: Nat Price, Victoria Dean

We would also like to thank all those who have offered help and advice along the way.

The Pocket Issue Team

Contents

One Minute Guide

The issues in the blink of an eye

ONE MINUTE GUIDE

Swans dying of bird flu in Dorset. MRSA deaths rocketing.
Headlines full of pandemic fears. But is an outbreak really likely?
Pocket Issue makes a diagnosis.

Is a pandemic a real possibility?

Pandemics – the rapid global spread of highly infectious and
dangerous diseases – are going on right now. Developing
countries continually battle against malaria, tuberculosis (TB)
and HIV/Aids. Health systems are under funded and
overstretched, although often supported by non-governmental
organisations (NGOs), non-profit making setups like Oxfam and
Médecins Sans Frontières.

That's dreadful. But, actually, I meant a bird flu pandemic.

Oh. You mean a pandemic that affects you. Birds infected with
H5N1, the deadly strain of avian flu (the correct term for bird flu)
have been found in the UK. Three swans were found dead in
Dorset in January 2008 and, periodically, poultry that may have
been in contact with an infected bird have been slaughtered as
a precautionary measure.

However, in the UK, there are no human deaths to date.
The UK government's verdict is that a bird flu pandemic
affecting humans is 'low risk' but would be 'high impact' if it
occurred. The World Health Organisation (WHO) considers
the current risk of pandemic influenza to be serious.

What has to happen to trigger a human bird flu pandemic?

At the moment, humans have to catch avian flu from direct
contact with infected birds. If the virus mutated to allow human-
to-human transmission, it could spread much more widely.

10

Is there any treatment if it does hit?
Tamiflu, an antiviral drug, is both a preventative medicine and a treatment for humans once bird flu is acquired. No one is certain that it would be effective if the virus mutates to allow human-to-human transmission. One science journal wrote that washing your hands regularly and wearing a facemask is at least as effective as Tamiflu in preventing the spread of bird flu.

What are the chances of an MRSA pandemic?
Cases of MRSA – an antibiotic-resistant superbug – are still rising dramatically. A drop in hospital hygiene, hospital overcrowding and the overuse of antibiotics are to blame. Preying on the vulnerable, MRSA makes hospitals a particularly dangerous place for the sick. Ironic…

Can it be treated?
Yes, but not that easily. A new antibiotic seems to be working.

What can the past tell us about pandemics?
That pandemics come and go. They always have – think the Black Death in the Middle Ages, or Spanish Flu, 1918-19 – and they always will. But in the past 100 years, three pandemics affecting the developed world have been avian flu-based, which is why bird flu is considered a threat. Apart from the 1918-19 pandemic, however, mortality rates were relatively low.

What can the past tell us about pandemics?
A future pandemic could be caused by a re-emergence of SARS (severe, acute respiratory syndrome), a severe type of pneumonia seen in Asia in 2003. Pandemics are hard to predict with real accuracy, and attempts at containment through isolation of infected cases, coupled with the most appropriate medical treatment to hand – ranging from drugs to vaccines – seem to be the best defences.

What would happen to the developed world in the event of a human bird flu pandemic?

Emergency pandemic plans would swing into action. Restrictions could be placed on movement and curfews introduced. Drugs and treatment would be rationed since resources are finite. Not everyone could be saved. At worst, there could be a million new cases a day in the UK, and mortuaries would be overwhelmed. The impact on the economy could be severe, depending on the duration and scale of the pandemic.

And the developing world?

With the developing world having far less access to medicines and with health systems already strained, casualty figures could be much higher than in the developed world.

Should I be worrying?

A human bird flu pandemic is a serious risk, according to the WHO. MRSA is only a real threat to those who are already vulnerable. One thing that is clear is that the people who face the biggest pandemic threats are those in developing countries who live with diseases, which, in the West, with better resources, are well managed, and therefore not pandemics at all.

Do I need to be concerned about global pandemics that don't physically affect me?

Yes. It's a small world with easy travel routes spanning the globe. Healthcare is increasingly a global issue.

ESPRESSO

So the coffee is being passed around the table, your hostess is looking serene, and the conversation turns to pandemics. Things you should (or shouldn't) say if you want to be asked again:

Have a second helping

"The chicken was delicious…and cooking it thoroughly definitely kills the H5N1 virus, I read it in Pocket Issue, the series that comprehensively covers hot, topical issues."

"The world really is a small place…so good healthcare means global healthcare."

"I'm donating a sum of money to Médecins Sans Frontières instead of sending Christmas cards this year."

"According to the British Medical Journal, washing your hands regularly and wearing masks might be more effective than drugs in preventing the spread of bird flu."

Get your coat

"I hope you cooked the chicken thoroughly…I'm too young to die"

"What you don't know doesn't hurt you. Ignorance is bliss!"

"Atish-ooo. Oh, so sorry, I've had a terrible cold. Bread? 'Scuse fingers'.

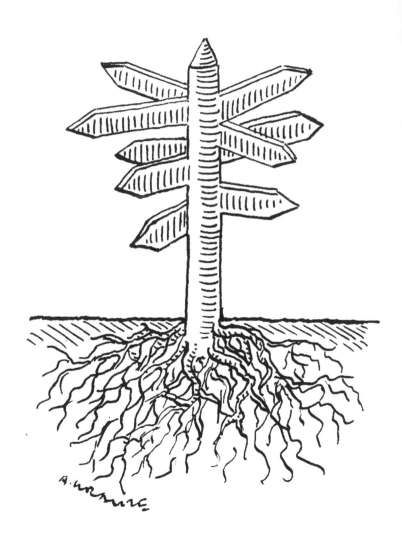

Roots

The important questions answered

THE ROOTS

PANDEMICS – WHAT'S THE ISSUE?
What is bird flu? Is it a real threat to our health? Are we really 'due' another pandemic, or is it just scaremongering? And if you go into hospital, are you likely to get MRSA and become very ill or even die? Has MRSA really spread into the community, meaning you can catch it in the gym or the supermarket?

Pandemic possibles?
If bird flu and MRSA are the current Big Two pandemic possibles, there's also the newly talked about Clostridium difficile (also known as C. difficile), another increasingly emerging, antibiotic-resistant hospital plague, not to mention all the other pandemics that still circulate around the world like invisible, ravenous beasts – Aids, malaria, even TB.

True or false?
Are these real threats, or are they just talked up in what is actually an ever-safer world? For at the same time as being scared witless about, most particularly, bird flu or MRSA, most people know that life expectancy in the 21st century is longer than ever before. So where does truth and a balanced view lie?

A BRIEF HISTORY – PANDEMICS
Ring-a-ring-a-roses is the nursery rhyme often associated with London's Great Plague of 1666, and 18th and 19th century literature is full of people coughing to death with TB, or consumption as it was called then. Just two examples of past pandemics that have affected life so intensely they have entered the realms of everyday culture. Pocket Issue asks how and why this happens.

What is a pandemic?
The word pandemic is derived from the Greek for 'all the people'. While an epidemic is a widespread outbreak of disease occurring in a single community or geographical region, a pandemic occurs on a much greater scale, spreading around the world and affecting hundreds of thousands of people across many countries.

The WHO defines a pandemic as the emergence of a disease new to the population, which infects humans easily and sustainably, and causes serious illness.

Have pandemics always occurred?
Yes. There have been many pandemics down the ages, from Typhoid in the Peloponnesian War in 430 BC, to the Spanish Flu of 1918-19 and more recently, Aids.

How do pandemics spread around the world?
Trade routes and wars have always played a part. Moving goods and people can also inadvertently transport diseases. For example, the Spanish brought smallpox to the Americas, which wiped out up to 90% of the indigenous population over the following four centuries. Today, globalisation and the ease of movement around the world means increased pandemic potential. Healthcare now requires action on a global scale.

Are they predictable, in terms of where and when they may hit?
Not really. Although people say we are 'overdue' a pandemic, changing circumstances for example better hygiene and medicine, and clean water as well as the mutations of existing diseases and the rise of new ones, means it is impossible to predict the imminent emergence of a pandemic with absolute accuracy. The Bubonic Plague made its first appearance in Egypt in 541 AD, and by

Healthcare now requires action on a global scale

17

700 AD had caused Europe's population to drop by 50%. However, it then disappeared for eight hundred years without anyone understanding why, before re-emerging in the Middle Ages.

Experts have been predicting a flu epidemic for years

Do we track pandemics when they happen?
Yes. Through epidemiology, the study of how diseases are caused, spread and controlled.

What are the most likely pandemics to strike the developed world at the moment?
Bird flu and MRSA. Experts have been predicting a flu epidemic for years, and the recurring threat of bird flu keeps getting them excited. And MRSA risks becoming a pandemic because of its rapid spread in the last few years.

Why is bird flu seen as such a pandemic possible?
In the last 100 years, pandemics in the developed world have been influenza-linked. The 1918-19 Spanish Flu, which was the last major pandemic, began as a flu that affected birds, and ended up killing 20 million people.

Any other threats?
Clostridium difficile, or C. difficile, is another antibiotic resistant hospital plague that seems to be spreading through British hospitals, and may over time become as big a threat as MRSA.

What pandemic threats does the developing world face?
Diseases that are treatable with the right medicines and health resources are still at pandemic level in the developing world. Aids, TB, malaria and polio are examples.

Does global warming affect the development of pandemics?
Changing climates can allow diseases to colonise new areas.

For example, as Britain warms up, the malaria carrying mosquito could become a possibility. And disasters that can be laid at the door of global warming – fresh water shortages, famines or flooding, create emergency conditions, with poor hygiene and overcrowding, that allow diseases to flourish.

Does intensive farming affect pandemics?

The drive for density and efficiency in livestock production has contributed to the development of virulent antibiotic resistant bacteria and viruses such as "Mad Cow" disease and foot and mouth. Intensive animal husbandry, and the transportation of animals across large distances, have increased the risk of global pandemics affecting humans developing from livestock. Currently, wealth creation in a global economy has been prioritised above risk management.

Can pandemics ever be eradicated?

Yes. In theory all infectious diseases could be eradicated. In reality, the changing nature of a disease means medicines and vaccines are not effective for long enough periods to prevent it spreading. The Carter Center, established by former US President, Jimmy Carter, is one major organisation that looks into which diseases could feasibly be eradicated.

A BRIEF HISTORY – THE ISSUES

Pandemics have been around since the year dot.

Trade routes and passenger travel facilitate the spread of diseases.

We can track pandemics as they develop, but we can't entirely accurately predict what threat will come to fruition at any given time.

Intensive farming of poultry, in particular, has increased the risk of a global pandemic that affects humans developing from livestock.

A.KRAUZE

BIRD FLU – THE RISKS, TREATMENTS AND MANAGEMENT PLANS

Are migrating birds going to infect our chickens with bird flu? Will the disease then jump species to infect humans via person-to-person transmission, bringing a pandemic to our doorstep? And if so, what is the outlook for us? Pocket Issue assembles the hard facts.

What is bird flu?

Avian Influenza, commonly known as bird flu, is a contagious viral disease in animals, caused by a number of strains of the Influenza A virus, which are endemic in birds. Of the many strains, H5N, the most lethal kind, is the one that is currently causing concern.

But why should we be worried if it's a disease that affects birds?

Because bird flu is increasingly infecting other species. It is loosely related to human influenza, and there is the potential to transmit the disease to humans. This has already happened in a limited

> By early 2008 there had been 359 cases of bird flu worldwide and 226 deaths

way, with some people catching the disease directly from birds.

Can bird flu be passed between humans?
There is little or no evidence that the change that would give a green light to a potential pandemic – the virus mutating to allow transmission from human-to-human – has happened.

When did bird flu start?
Outbreaks of bird flu have been reported in several countries throughout Asia since 2003.

How many people have been affected?
As of February 2008, there have been a reported 359 cases of bird flu worldwide and 226 deaths.

How dangerous is the current strain of H5N1?
Approximately 60% of humans known to have been infected with the current strain of HN51 have died from it. This mortality rate is much higher than for common flu.

So could the virus trigger a pandemic?
Only specific mutations will make it more infectious to humans. For example, if the virus infects a human or animal that is already carrying human influenza, the two viruses could mix, producing a strain that is lethal and highly infectious to humans.

> The WHO considers the risk of pandemic human influenza to be serious

So it's a risk but not a certainty?
It's very hard to predict. In 2005, Sir Liam Donaldson, England's Chief Medical

Officer, said "We do not know what the virus is that will cause pandemic flu. What we do know is that Mother Nature has the recipe book and it's just a matter of time before she starts cooking."

However, Sir David King, the outgoing Government Chief Scientist, labelled human bird flu a "low risk", but with "high impact" if it does occur.

What we do know is that, according to the WHO, there is mounting evidence that the H5N1 strain has a unique capacity to jump the species barrier and cause severe disease, with high mortality, in humans. The WHO considers the risk of pandemic human influenza to be serious.

Where is bird flu occurring?
Mostly in Asia. Since 2003, when bird flu began, millions of Asian birds have died after contracting the disease, or been destroyed to prevent it spreading.

H5N1 can kill an entire flock of birds within forty-eight hours

Are domestic birds more vulnerable to bird flu than wild birds?
Yes, domestically bred birds like chickens and turkeys seem more vulnerable to dying from bird flu than wild birds, which often carry the virus with no obvious symptoms.

What are the symptoms of bird flu in poultry?
Birds can die without any warning or obvious signs of illness. Signs of illness, if they do appear, include swollen heads, low egg production and loss of appetite. H5N1 can kill an entire flock of birds within forty-eight hours.

What are the symptoms of bird flu in humans?
To date, these seem similar to common flu – a high temperature, coughing, muscle

aches, eye infections and a sore throat – but within three days, serious respiratory problems develop and the patient deteriorates. If the disease becomes transmissible between people, these symptoms could alter, becoming less ferocious to allow widespread transmission between humans. This is necessary because for a disease to spread efficiently, it can't kill its victims too quickly.

Why have the outbreaks mostly emerged in Asia?
Much of the population lives in closer quarters with their animals, and this allows different flu viruses to mix, develop new strains and pass between the species. Almost all those who have been infected with H5N1 had extensive physical contact with infected birds.

Where else is bird flu occurring?
As of 2007, H5N1 in animals had been recorded in over 50 countries – in Asia, Africa and Europe, including France, Italy,

Germany, Greece, Austria, Hungary, Slovenia, Slovakia and Britain.

How has it spread so widely?
Traditionally, pandemics spread quickly through global trade routes. With poultry flocks being moved for trade purposes, this can be a factor. Migrating birds can also transport the virus, and obviously there is an uncontrollable element to this. These threats have led to most countries adopting the Avian Influenza Directive.

The Avian Influenza Directive?
An EU initiative that increases surveillance of flocks and introduces powers to restrict animal movements.

Can birds be vaccinated?
China tried it, but the vaccine failed to prevent low-level infections, allowing the virus to spread widely without obvious mass deaths in birds. However, other countries are exploring this option further.

23

January 2008, three swans were found dead in Dorset, struck down by H5N1

Is there any other way of combating H5N1?

Not really – and there is a lot of poultry to keep an eye on. China and other East Asian countries have seen an explosion in meat production, much of which is on small farms where poultry often mingle with wild birds. This offers many opportunities for the virus to jump species and adapt to poultry. Monitoring outbreaks and trying to deal with them through culling and containment currently seems the best form of control.

How has Britain been affected so far?

On the 30th January 2007 turkeys at a Bernard Matthews farm in Holton, Suffolk, began to die – 800 within two days. When the state veterinary service was called in, the 159,000 flock was diagnosed with H5N1 and slaughtered. A further outbreak of bird flu in the autumn of 2007 in flocks of chickens and turkeys in Suffolk led to mass slaughtering of birds. The Government gave the all clear just weeks before Christmas. In January 2008, three swans were found dead in Dorset, struck down by H5N1.

What is the government's plan to detect the arrival of bird flu?

Surveillance is a key tool: The Department for Environment, Food and Rural Affairs (DEFRA) has asked birdwatchers to help look out for the arrival of the infection.

Scientists are also examining bird droppings for signs of the influenza virus. The EU is advocating constant and open communication between the public, vets and doctors to alert the authorities about outbreaks. For example, anyone who spots an unusual number of dead wild birds should contact the

DEFRA helpline (see glossary for details) before taking action. The public are advised not to handle bird carcasses unless it is essential to do so.

What happens if a bird is identified as having bird flu?
A control zone is set up around the area in which the bird was discovered. Authorities slaughter poultry that may have been in contact with the infected bird, in an attempt to contain the spread of the virus. During a period of infection, movement of poultry flocks is restricted to reduce the chance of the virus spreading. This kind of prevention is a key tactic in stopping the virus from mutating and becoming a pandemic.

What happens if infected birds aren't spotted and their meat finds its way into the food chain?
Cooking infected meat seems to kill the virus. There is no evidence that eating infected meat is dangerous. However, the Food Standards Agency recommends that meat and

At the peak of the pandemic 1 million could be infected in a day

eggs are well cooked. The Australian government has recommended washing eggs before breaking them and washing hands afterwards.

What would be the likely impact on Britain of a human bird flu pandemic?
The Department of Health (DoH) contingency plan suggests that between 21,000 and 700,000 deaths could be expected in Britain from a human flu pandemic.

Such a wide-ranging estimate illustrates the difficulties in accurately predicting the outcome of a pandemic. One quarter of the population could become infected, and another quarter would need to care for them. At the peak of the pandemic 1 million could be infected in a day.

Where will the response to the crisis be directed from?
The DoH would be responsible for co-ordinating the emergency response in the UK, supported by the Health Protection Agency (HPA), the national authority responsible for dealing with the spread of infectious disease. The DoH would establish a national operations room to support the local response to outbreaks and co-ordinate vaccine distribution to affected areas.

The HPA would be the nerve centre of operations – it would set up a strategic emergency co-ordination centre, and co-ordinate clinical surveillance, providing infection control advice, analysing flu strains and issuing information to public and healthcare professionals. Other government ministries would report to the DoH.

What contribution would local communities make?
Local communities will respond to strategic direction from the DoH. They may also have to deal with a range of problems, rather than looking to the government. Schools, international NGOs and corporations all have strategies in place.

What restrictions would be imposed on the population?
There would probably be quarantines, travel restrictions and closures of schools and public meetings. The police would probably be granted major emergency powers in accordance with the 2004 Civil Contingencies Act.

What else could we expect to happen?
A leaked British Cabinet report indicated that local authorities might not be able to rely on armed forces, that effective vaccines might not be available until well into the pandemic, and that the death toll might overwhelm mortuaries.

What about the financial impact?
Already, governments around the world are spending billions

> World Bank estimates that up to US$2 trillion could be lost

of dollars planning for the pandemic, buying medicines, running disaster drills and planning strategies for tighter border control. US$10 billion has already been lost and 200 million birds killed in an attempt to contain bird flu.

In the event of the human pandemic becoming a reality, the World Bank estimates that up to US$2 trillion could be lost – that's a loss of up to 5% of global GDP.

And the impact on the poultry industry?
Poultry sales and prices have already fallen globally in response to reduced demand. Many poultry farmers in developing countries can't afford the measures necessary to prevent their livestock having any contact with wild birds, and have simply stopped cooperating with efforts to deal with the flu, risking their lives and livelihoods. Other farmers, in countries where no compensation is paid for the slaughter of stock, have lost their livelihoods.

Who's most at risk of catching bird flu in the event of a human pandemic?
The elderly and the very young – as with common flu – will be vulnerable to human bird flu. But avian flu can also provoke a strong immune system into over-reacting to a threat and cause healthy individuals in the prime of their lives to become fatally ill. This is called a **cytokine storm**.

> Cytokine storms can damage organs and tissue within the body, sometimes fatally

What is a cytokine storm?

Cytokines activate the immune cells to do the fighting, but can sometimes activate too many. Cytokine storms can damage organs and tissue within the body, sometimes fatally. For example, if a cytokine storm occurs in the lungs, fluids and immune cells accumulate and block the airways, which can lead to death. Human deaths from H5N1 have usually involved cytokine storms.

What treatments are there against human bird flu:

Is there a vaccine?

Vaccines have been developed, and are the first line of defence for vulnerable groups of the population. However, there is no vaccine against the precise strain that might be responsible for the pandemic.

Are there any drugs?

Tamiflu is the main antiviral drug used to treat bird flu, from a group of drugs called neuraminidase inhibitors. Produced by Swiss pharmaceutical company Roche, Tamiflu has been used before to combat bird flu. It is unclear how effective it will be against human bird flu.

How does Tamiflu work?

It seems to be able to stop some people from being infected at all, and helps others who have already contracted bird flu to recover more quickly. However, it is not without side effects. These may include mental disorder and delusions, particularly in teenagers. In June 2007, the Japanese health ministry found that more than 1300 people had exhibited neuropsychiatric symptoms since the drug went on sale in Japan in 2001. Some 71 of these had died.

Tamiflu has a relatively short shelf life – a maximum of 36 months

Is Tamiflu widely available?

No. It is available in the UK but only on prescription. There is not enough of it for everyone, as governments around the world have placed orders, stockpiling the drug in case of a pandemic. It might be possible to buy it online, but since prices have increased the British government has warned that fakes are in circulation.

Does Tamiflu date?
Yes. Tamiflu has a relatively short shelf life – a maximum of 36 months, which means that stocks have to be updated regularly.

Are there any other drug treatments effective against human bird flu?
Another class of antiviral drugs, the most common of which is Relenza, may also be effective. However, they have more drawbacks than Tamiflu. Relenza, for example, has to be inhaled and is harder to store over long periods.

How effective will antiviral drugs be in combating a human bird flu pandemic?
It's difficult to say. Governments around the world are stockpiling Tamiflu and

Relenza to control future pandemics. But there are worries about people becoming resistant to drugs. For example, in December 2005, research published by the New England Journal of Medicine showed that two out of eight patients being treated for bird flu in Vietnam died despite receiving Tamiflu.

The worst-case scenario sounds bleak. A case of Britain facing a "high impact" event, with little border control to prevent spread and not enough drugs to fight it?
That's not the spirit. Think Blitz mentality and cups of tea in times of crisis. Think Churchill. 'We'll fight them on the beaches'. And remember, there's still debate over whether it will happen at all. While the WHO says it's not if but when, Sir David King, the outgoing UK Government Scientist, declared it a "low risk". Either way, Britain and most European countries have carefully laid emergency plans (although untested), and have ordered plenty of Tamiflu.

BIRD FLU – THE ISSUES

Bird flu is spreading globally. If the virus mutates, allowing person-to-person transmission, it will probably be less deadly but spread quickly.

Sir David King, outgoing Government Chief Scientist, considers the risk "low" but if it should happen, the impact will be "high".

Cytokine storms – when the body's immune system overreacts – have been a key cause of past human deaths.

Governments across Europe have emergency plans in place.

Treatments exist for bird flu, but they are only partially effective and of limited supply.

MRSA – THE RISKS, TREATMENTS AND MANAGEMENT PLANS

What is this so-called 'superbug'? How is it spreading, and what, if anything, can we do to contain it, and to protect ourselves? Pocket Issue scrubs up and takes a look.

What is MRSA?
Methicillin-resistant Staphylococcus aureus (MRSA) is a bacterium that causes difficult to treat infections. It is a more resistant variation of the common bacteria Staphylococcus aureus.

When did MRSA start?
MRSA was discovered in the UK in 1961, and is now found worldwide. Scientists have found 17 strains of MRSA, each with differing degrees of drug resistance.

Which strains are found In the UK?
In the UK, the most common strains of MRSA are MRSA-15 and MRSA-16.

And where is MRSA found?
It is estimated that between 20-40% of people in the UK carry MRSA, mostly in the nose or on the skin. MRSA is also found in hospitals and in the community.

Hospital MRSA:
this strain of MRSA is the most prevalent type of hospital-acquired infection in England - making up around 44% of all cases, striking around 100,000 people a year and costing the NHS £1 billion.

Community-acquired MRSA:
this strain is relatively harmless, causing boils and minor infections.

Hospital MRSA strikes around 100,000 people a year and costs the NHS £1 billion

31

So hospital-MRSA is the most deadly type of MRSA?
Apart from the rarer 'Killer' MRSA and VRSA (see below), yes.

What are the symptoms?
Boils, abscesses, sties, carbuncles, impetigo, in the first instance. However, if MRSA enters the bloodstream, through an open wound or a catheter, more serious problems include septicaemia (blood poisoning), septic shock, joint problems, bone marrow infection, lung infection and infection of the heart lining.

Why is it so dangerous?
Because it is able to survive treatment by antibiotics of the beta-lactam type - this includes penicillin and methicillin. This resistance to antibiotics is why MRSA is often called a 'superbug' in the press, and what makes it very dangerous when it infects vulnerable people, such as patients in hospital.

What is antibiotic resistance?
It is the ability of a micro-organism to withstand the effects of an antibiotic. Antibiotic resistance develops naturally via natural selection and random mutation. The variants of the bacteria able to resist antibiotics are the ones that survive, producing increasingly resistant populations of bacteria. Bacteria pass on resistance genes to other bacteria through a process known as 'plasmid exchange'. When a bacterium has several resistance genes it is 'multi-resistant'.

Antibiotic usage affects the development of bacterial resistance

How does this resistance develop?
Research shows that antibiotic usage affects the development of bacterial resistance. Overuse of broad-spectrum antibiotics (antibiotics which act against a wide-range of bacteria as opposed to only specific

families of bacteria) significantly enables the development of antibiotic resistant bacteria. Other factors that contribute include the improper use of antibiotics by patients (such as not completing courses), unnecessary use of medication and prescriptions, and the routine use of antibiotics in farming.

Are cases of MRSA on the rise?
Yes. In 1991, MRSA was responsible for 4% of fatal cases of blood poisoning in UK hospitals. By 1999 this had risen to 37%.

How prevalent is MRSA in hospitals?
It is reaching epidemic levels. According to government figures, cases of MRSA in England and Wales have increased by 600% in the past decade – though the Office for National Statistics states that deaths involving MRSA have stabilised at around 1,650 recorded in 2005 and 2006.

A total of 1,168 people had MRSA recorded on their death certificate as a principal cause of death or a contributory factor in 2004, a rise of 213 from the previous year.

How deadly is MRSA?
Units: Number of recorded deaths with MRSA cited as underlying cause in England and Wales, 1993-2005.

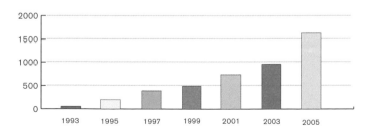

Source: Office of National Statistics

How is MRSA spread from a carrier to another person?
Dispersal of MRSA from the nose, either through sneezing, or by transferring the bugs to the hands or communally used equipment, is the main way the bacteria spreads.

Why is MRSA spreading through hospitals?
This is down to inadequate cleaning and hygiene procedures on the part of hospital staff. This allows MRSA bacterial colonies to transfer from patient to patient. Some of this is almost unavoidable. For example, health workers who lean over MRSA carrying patients often pick up the germs on their hands or clothing and carry it to the next patient. And blood pressure cuffs used by nurses on patients' bare arms often carry bacteria including MRSA. In a French teaching hospital study, 77% of blood pressure cuffs moved around the hospital were contaminated with MRSA.

What cleaning methods combat MRSA in hospitals?
Alcohol and chlorine bleach are effective sanitisers against MRSA. Vaporised sanitisers are increasingly being used in Intensive Care and Emergency.

How much of a problem is community-acquired MRSA?
Over the past decade, new strains of MRSA have emerged in the community, causing infections in young, otherwise healthy people. Truly community-based MRSA appears to differ in its genetic make up from that found in hospital environments. But it is difficult to separate true community-based MRSA from MRSA that people out in the community may have acquired from a health care setting, as an outpatient, from hospitalisation, nursing home admission or from close contact with people in these settings.

Do all carriers of community-acquired MRSA have symptoms?
No – strains of Staphylococcus

aureus are able to colonise their hosts for long periods of time before causing infections.

Isn't there something called 'Killer' MRSA?
Yes. A rare mutation of C-MRSA produces the lethal toxin Panton-Valentine Leukocidin (PVL), which killed the 18 year old Royal Marine Richard Campbell-Smith in November 2004. PVL destroys white blood cells, leaving the immune system too weak to fight the infection. Symptoms include pneumonia, very high temperatures and coughing up blood. Only a quarter of victims survive PVL if it spreads to the lungs. It was thought the disease had been eradicated in the 1950s, but a microbiologist who gave evidence at Mr Campbell-Smith's inquest said she had seen two cases of PVL in nine weeks.

And VRSA?
Another rare strain of MRSA, which is resistant to Vancomycin, the antibiotic used to treat MRSA when other drugs have failed.

So how can MRSA be treated?
Through the application of oral agents such as Linezolid, Doxycycline or Minocycline.

Maggots have been used to successfully treat MRSA patients in record time

New antibiotics:
In May 2006, researchers from Merck Pharmaceuticals reported that they had discovered a new type of antibiotic called Platensimycin that could be used successfully against MRSA. However MRSA could develop a resistance to this, too.

Maggot therapy:
Maggots used in larval therapy have been used to help successfully treat MRSA patients in record time. A study at the University of Manchester found that bottle fly larvae cured diabetics with foot ulcers contaminated with MRSA in an

35

average of three weeks – compared to 28 weeks for conventional treatment. Maggots have been used since the Napoleonic Wars to eat dead tissue and bacteria, leaving healthy tissue to heal, but were phased out with the introduction of antibiotics around 80 years ago. They are also more cost-effective than comparable antibacterial remedies, such as courses of hydrogel.

Phage therapy:
This is an approach extensively researched and used in the Soviet Union, and also in the US, until the discovery of antibiotics. Phages are 'viruses' (more properly known as bacteriophages) that invade bacterial cells and cause bacteria to destruct.

So there are ways to treat MRSA?
Yes. And these can be developed further. The use of a biodegradable preparation that can continually release bacteriophages to destroy Staphylococcus aureus might become an important alternative to antibiotics in an era of multi-resistant 'superbugs'. Phages also have few side effects compared to antibiotics.

Plants can also provide many antibacterial medicinal compounds and scientific studies have shown that many plant products can inhibit pathogenic bacteria, in ways distinct to antibiotics.

Finally, there could be further antibiotic development. However, this is hampered by lack of funding for antibiotic research due to decreases in industry budgets and lack of sponsorship from government.

What is the NHS doing to combat MRSA?
In the mid 1990s, the NHS used 'search and destroy' to combat MRSA. This involved isolating all patients with MRSA, and screening all staff and removing them from work until they had eradication therapy.

The 'Clean your Hands'

campaign: Since August 2004, NHS wards must place alcohol-based hand rubs near all beds and at the entrance to wards to encourage staff and visitors to wash their hands more regularly. The Health Act 2006 introduced a statutory hygiene code for hospital and care homes in England, which is enforced by the Healthcare Commission.

> The number of cleaners in the NHS fell from 100,000 in 1984 to 55,000 in 2004

Why have attempts to control MRSA failed in the past?
Because patients with MRSA present, but the symptoms not yet apparent, are discharged and then readmitted. If the number of patients in the community reaches a certain threshold, the search and destroy strategy becomes ineffective. And a failure of hygiene measures. Public Service union Unison estimates that the number of cleaners in the NHS fell from 100,000 in 1984 to 55,000 in 2004.

And most recently?
Prime Minister Gordon Brown pledged to 'deep clean' hospital wards room by room. But with MRSA having risen significantly since hospital cleaning was contracted out, some critics say bring back Matron, who would supposedly never have allowed standards to fall so severely in the first place.

How have other countries dealt with MRSA?
United States: alongside the UK, the US has one of the worst records of combating drug-resistant infections. Hence between 1976 and 2003, MRSA hospital infections increased 32 times, according to the Centers for Disease Prevention and Control in the US.

However, pilot programmes using hygiene precautions, as run by the Presbyterian University Hospital in

Pittsburgh, reduced MRSA infections by 90 per cent.

The Netherlands:
The Netherlands seems to have dealt more successfully with MRSA than the UK. Eradication therapy for MRSA is carried out upon a patient's discharge from hospital.

How could the NHS improve its current efforts to combat MRSA?
By introducing universal testing of patients for MRSA. The MRSA test costs no more than an HIV test, and is less invasive, involving only a nasal or skin swab. And by requiring health care workers to wear gowns.

Would this be too expensive to be viable?
It is expensive, but allowing MRSA infections to continue leads to longer hospital stays for patients who develop infections. Prevention can look less expensive when compared to this. For example, a pilot programme at the University of Pittsburgh, USA, found that providing universal screening tests and gowns for healthcare workers cost around $35,000 a year, but saved more than US$800,000.

And of course, most importantly, these precautions saved lives.

MRSA – THE ISSUES

MRSA is a largely antibiotic resistant germ that is particularly prevalent in hospitals.

In 1993, the superbug caused 51 deaths, up to 1,629 in 2005. The sick and the ill are particularly vulnerable.

Along with the US, the UK has one of the worst records of dealing with MRSA.

Cleanliness, the development of new antibiotics, and a range of other therapies are the best defence against this so-called 'super bug'.

OTHER CURRENT PANDEMICS – TB, MALARIA, HIV/AIDS AND MORE

Malaria, HIV/Aids and TB are three pandemics that have been on-going for years. Today, they are too often diseases of poverty, with overcrowding, poor sanitation and poor diet facilitating their spread. Developing nations account for 95% of the global Aids prevalence, 98% of active tuberculosis infections, while 90% of malaria deaths occur in sub-Saharan Africa. Diseases of poverty kill somewhere in the region of 14 million people a year. Pocket Issue finds out more.

TUBERCULOSIS OR TB:

What is TB?
TB is a serious bacterial infection, caused by a germ called Mycobacterium tuberculosis. It most usually affects the lungs. A person is most likely to develop it if they have a weak immune system and are already in poor health.

> Some 15 million Americans are infected with TB

Is it really a pandemic? Didn't TB die out with Charles Dickens?
Unfortunately TB is very much a presence in the 21st century. It is on the rise, and fulfils the WHO pandemic criteria: it is spreading, is highly infectious, and kills: currently, about 2 million people a year. That's one person every 15 seconds.

Where is it found?
Mainly in the developing world. However, cases are on the rise in the UK from an all time low in the 1980s. Around 350 people die from TB in England each year. Some 15 million Americans are infected with TB.

Why are cases on the rise in developed countries?
Due to a combination of factors, including increases in poverty, immigration from areas where TB is common, increased travel and exposure

to TB, and Aids (TB is common in those with Aids, the most advanced form of HIV).

How is TB spread?
It spreads through coughing and sneezing. TB bacteria are coughed or sneezed into the air by those with active TB. The bacteria are carried in the air, and if a person breathes in some TB bacteria they may then multiply in the lungs, leading to a TB infection. However, close contact and repeated exposure to someone with active TB is usually required.

> Left untreated, about half of active TB sufferers die

What are the symptoms?
It can be asymptomatic. In this case the immune system fights the infection in the lungs, sometimes leaving a scar on the lungs. Active TB starts with a dry cough, which can continue for months, slowly worsening. Bloodstained phlegm can be coughed up.

Other symptoms include fevers, sweats, weight loss and breathlessness.

How deadly is the disease?
With treatment, it is not deadly at all. But left untreated, about half of active TB sufferers die.

What is the treatment and can it be cured?
A six month course of antibiotics can treat most cases. But this kind of sustained treatment, although relatively inexpensive, is difficult to administer in the developing world, with already over strained health systems.

What about a vaccine?
Work is being done on improving TB vaccines. The BCG, most effective in children, provides more than 70% protection. However, some people still develop TB despite having had the vaccine.

MALARIA:

What is malaria?
Malaria is an infectious disease caused by protozoan (single

cell) parasites transmitted to humans via mosquitoes, which infect through their bite. It is widespread in tropical and subtropical regions such as the Americas, Asia and Africa.

Malaria kills around 2 million people a year and possibly many more

Is it a pandemic?
Most definitely. Malaria kills around 2 million people a year and possibly many more. The Centers for Disease Control and Prevention estimate 5.3 million malaria deaths annually. However it tends to go unnoticed in the developed world. The impact of malaria on Africa alone qualifies it for pandemic status.

Dr Wencelaus Kilama, Chairman of Malaria Foundation International said: "The Malaria epidemic is like loading up seven Boeing 747 airliners each day, and crashing them into Mount Kilimanjaro."

What are the symptoms?
Tingling in the skin, fever and chills and other flu-like symptoms. If it is not treated, in its most advanced stages it brings on coma and then death.

What are the treatments?
Preventative drugs can be taken when visiting an area where malaria is in circulation. However these are mainly for travellers and short term visitors. They aren't practical for residents in malaria endemic areas because of their side effects from long term use and because they are too expensive for people living in the most afflicted areas – the developing world.

Anti-malarial drugs such as quinine or artemisinin derivatives can be taken once malaria is acquired, but unfortunately drug resistance is becoming increasingly common.

What is being done to control or eradicate malaria?
Public initiatives include pest

management, for example by spraying insecticides on mosquito breeding grounds, feeding and resting locations, as well as the use of insecticide at night and DDT-treated bed nets.

However mosquitoes are developing a resistance to pesticides and the DDT-treated bed nets, although effective, need re-impregnating every six months and that is expensive. Other methods include improved housing construction methods to prevent mosquito entry, for example using mosquito screens on windows.

DDT was vital in eradicating malaria in Brazil and Egypt

Isn't the use of DDT controversial?

Yes, there is a major debate over DDT. It damages biodiversity by killing other species and mosquito resistance to it would increase rapidly with its large scale use. On the other hand, it was vital in eradicating the disease in Brazil and Egypt.

So why isn't insecticide used to obliterate mosquitoes once and for all?

Many African countries have advocated (and sometimes implemented) increased access to DDT for years, saying that the toll of human lives lost by not using the pesticide far outweighs potential environmental risks of using it.

And some development advocates criticise countries that are already developed for holding double standards when it comes to DDT – having used it locally in the past to eradicate malaria but now opposing its use by developing countries.

Also, there's mosquito resistance to consider: After exposure to insecticides such as DDT over several generations, high levels of resistance can arise. And resistance can build up rapidly given the mosquito's short life expectancy, severely limiting the effectiveness of the insecticide.

How might malaria be eradicated in the future?
Scientists are studying an immune response in some mosquitoes that kills the plasmodium parasites after they have invaded the mosquito stomach.

It is hoped that one day, genetically modified mosquitoes with this immune response will replace the wild mosquito, limiting or possibly even eliminating the transmission of malaria.

What about a malaria vaccine?
Researchers have been working on a vaccine for malaria for more than 20 years without success.

Could malaria reappear in the developed world?
The Centers for Disease Control and Prevention warn that the Anopheles species of mosquitoes, which live in colder climates, can transmit

malaria not only in areas where it is endemic, but also where it has been eliminated. So there is a risk of the re-introduction of the disease, which should not be ignored with climate change now an accepted reality due to global warming.

HIV/AIDS:

What is HIV/Aids?
Human Immunodeficiency Virus (HIV) is a virus that attacks the cells of the immune system, which over time reduces the body's ability to defend itself against various illnesses.

At this point, Acquired Immunodeficiency Syndrome (Aids) develops. This is the most advanced stage of HIV infection.

Aids has killed more than 25 million people since 1981

Is HIV a pandemic?
Yes. It has killed more than 25 million people since 1981, making it one of the most

43

destructive pandemics in world history. There are an estimated 32 million infected with it worldwide. In terms of killer diseases WHO figures show Aids to be out in front as a major cause of death over the next 20 years. *(see chart below)*

What is the treatment?
Since 1995, and the introduction of antiretroviral drugs, which suppress HIV, the outlook for sufferers has improved considerably. They do not cure HIV, but they slow it and even stop it. The medications must be taken regularly and exactly as prescribed in order to suppress HIV, maintain the immune system and stop the virus becoming resistant to the drugs.

Are there any side effects?
Yes. But before the introduction of antiretroviral drugs a person with HIV usually did not survive for more than two years. With drugs, the disease can be arrested.

> An HIV infected person can remain without symptoms for 8 to 9 years

Is there a vaccine for HIV?
More than 20 years of research, and a vaccine is still proving elusive.

How is HIV spread?
Most commonly, through sex with an infected person. Although it was initially associated with the gay

Projected deaths for killer diseases worldwide over the next 20 years
Units: million deaths

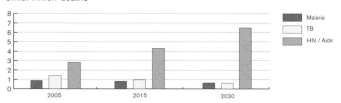

Source: World Health Organisation

community, heterosexual intercourse in the primary mode of HIV infection worldwide. Other ways of infection include: needle sharing by drug users; infected blood transfusions (this is rare in a developed country where blood is screened for HIV before being used, but a major problem in developing countries); from mother to child through pregnancy or breastfeeding.

Can it be passed through day-to-day contact?
No. Touching, sharing food, kissing and so on does not transmit the virus.

What are the symptoms of HIV?
Two to six weeks after infection, many people develop symptoms similar to flu or glandular fever. Once this passes, a person can remain without symptoms for 8 to 9 years. Many people do not realise they have the virus, and they can still pass it on. However, a blood test will tell a person if they are infected.

> South Africa alone has an estimated 5.5 million HIV infections

What are the symptoms of Aids?
Someone with Aids has a very low immune system, and is therefore easy prey for opportunistic infections such as TB, thrush, eye infections, coughs, fevers and weight loss.

Without treatment, severe infections can prove fatal. There is also a higher risk of developing other conditions such as a number of cancers.

Where is HIV/Aids found?
Africa: A third of deaths due to HIV/Aids occur in sub-Saharan Africa. 60% of all people living with HIV worldwide live here. South Africa alone has an estimated 5.5 million infections.

Asia: Two-thirds of HIV/Aids infections in Asia occur in India, with an estimated 5.7 million infections.

Where is Aids the biggest killer?
Unit: percentage of total deaths by region.

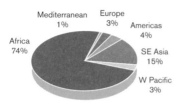

Mediterranean 1%
Europe 3%
Americas 4%
Africa 74%
SE Asia 15%
W Pacific 3%

Source: World Health Organisation

What about the US and Europe?

In the US, there are between 9,000 and 30,000 deaths due to HIV/Aids annually.

In Western and central Europe, this figure stands at between 12,000 and 15,000 deaths annually.

Why are there many less deaths in the developed world compared to the developing world?

This is due to widespread educational campaigns, the screening of blood transfusions and the use of condoms, as well as the development of effective, if expensive, drugs that suppress HIV.

And why is sub-Saharan Africa suffering so much?

Because of widespread STDs, poor nutrition and hygiene, and the hampering of sex education campaigns due to poverty.

Also, the expense of antiretroviral medication limits access for sufferers. And cultural denial has meant some countries have been slow to create antiretroviral programmes.

Cultural denial?

South Africa is an example. Resistance within the government to acknowledge the scale of the problem, refusing to believe that HIV alone caused Aids, rather blaming poverty and malnutrition. This meant years elapsed before the government began to respond properly to help sufferers.

Nelson Mandela's announcement in 2005 that his son had died of Aids was aimed at forcing South African then-president Thabo Mbeki out of this act of denial.

Can antiretroviral drugs be made more accessible? Research into antiretroviral drugs has focused on decreasing side effects and simplifying drug regimes, rather than reducing cost.

OTHER CURRENT PANDEMICS – THE ISSUES

Current pandemics of TB, HIV/Aids and malaria lead to millions of deaths in the developing world.

TB and HIV/Aids, which also affect the developed world, are controlled through drugs, education and proper funding of health programmes.

With the right funding and resources, TB and HIV/Aids are manageable diseases that need not reach pandemic proportions.

THE ETHICS OF PANDEMICS MANAGEMENT – WHO GETS DRUGS AND AT WHAT PRICE?

What are the ethical issues thrown up by a pandemic? With finite resources at a nation's disposal, who decides who gets saved, and on what basis? How great is the developed world's responsibility to assist the developing world? And is it ethical for the drug companies to be profiting from the production of life saving drugs? Pocket Issue explores these thorny issues.

WHO GETS SAVED?

Can life saving treatment really be rationed?

Rationing already happens in many healthcare systems. Although most healthcare systems in the developed world (apart from in the US) are based on universal rights to appropriate medical treatment, this does not prevent rationing, or the prioritising of acute treatments. This is simply a result of pressure on resources. During a pandemic, this pressure will be greater. Prioritising could then become a matter of life and death.

How is it decided who gets treatment and who doesn't?

Prioritising systems based on some criteria must be set up. For example, when vaccine supplies are limited, should children and elderly people, traditionally the most vulnerable, be first in the queue? Or should important workers and government ministers go ahead of everyone else, on the basis that they need to keep the country running while most of us drop like flies?

> Prioritising drugs could become a matter of life and death

That sounds horrible. Like taking one person off a life support machine to put another on. Is there any other way?

Not really, when there simply isn't enough of a resource to go around. It's just about which group of people take priority. In the US, planning for pandemic influenza was debated by the Advisory Committee on Immunisation Practices (ACIP). One approach considered was focusing on the 'life cycle principle'. This argued that rather than just thinking about saving the most lives when considering rationing, a better approach would be to maximise the individual's life span and opportunity. Under this principle, a 20 year old would be valued more than a one year old because the 20 year old would have developed more interests, hopes and plans, but would not have had an opportunity to realise them.

Given the impact these prioritising systems could have, shouldn't the public at least be consulted?

Yes. Pandemic preparations will work better if they are founded on widely held ethical values. Public consultation on such important policy issues is vital, as the public will need to help implement the procedures in an emergency pandemic state.

What about the ethics of pandemic planning on a global scale?

In today's global economy, with the criss-crossing of national boundaries, developing healthcare worldwide is vital. Developed countries have the advantage in terms of resources. Distributing some of these resources to the developing world is ethically responsible behaviour and would reduce the risk of the pandemic globally.

What does this mean the developed world could do?

Let's take the example of bird flu. Data on avian and pandemic influenza planning and response could be available to developing and developed countries and vaccines, antivirals and other public and social health interventions could be promoted for developing countries.

Are initiatives like this happening?

There are existing structures that support international healthcare initiatives, most notably the World Health Organisation, which works globally, and the European Centre for Disease Prevention and Control (ECDC) which has an EU remit. (For more on this see The Key Players).
But more could be done.

DRUGS:

Is it ethical to profit from the production of life-saving drugs?

Pharmaceutical companies are profit driven organisations. They use patents to prevent the copying and selling of products they have invented, and as a result the market price of medicines is out of reach for people in developing countries. This means that in the 1990s, HIV-infected individuals in developed countries could lead full lives because of antiretroviral drugs, but in developing countries patients were dying within months of diagnosis.

How have developing countries dealt with this life-and-death frustration?
India and Thailand have responded by producing low price copies of patented medicine called generics. These were made available in their own countries and also sold abroad.

Indian produced generic drugs for HIV/Aids treatment cost less than $200 per year

How steep is the price difference?
Very steep indeed. Indian produced generic drugs for HIV/Aids treatment cost less than $200 per year, when the named brand equivalent cost over $10,000. The affordability of generics means many more people can be treated. Indian generics have reached 40% of patients in the developing world. Some 90% of the antiretrovirals used in

Zimbabwe's Aids treatment programme come from India. Indian generic drugs have even helped the US President's Emergency Plan for Aids Relief (PEPFAR) to expand its access to Aids treatment. Some 33 of the 36 Aids drugs approved by the Food & Drug Administration for use in PEPFAR are produced in India.

Are generics identical to the brand named drug?
Yes, generics have to have the same ingredients as the original drug, and so are equally safe and effective.

Don't the patents held by the drug companies protect against generics?
Generics are usually produced after patents protecting the original drug have expired.

Why are they so cheap?
Generic companies do not have to fund research and clinical trials, and can just reverse engineer the existing drug. So with lower costs,

51

> Without the profit motive the patented drug may never have been developed in the first place

their prices can be substantially lower.

What do the drug companies think of generics?
Generics obviously affect profits. Drug companies maintain they need to defend their profits in order to be able to have funds to re-invest in research. This may be the case, and without the profit motive the patented drug may never have been developed in the first place, but it doesn't help the developing world.

What is the justification for generics?
Pharmaceuticals are putting profits before patients. It has been argued that major drug companies have large profit margins and can afford to lose

the revenue affected by generics. Drug companies also invest mostly in innovations that will bring the highest return. These can be life style drugs marketed to rich countries, rather than life saving drugs that meet the needs of poor people in developing countries.

So more is invested in drugs that fight obesity and incontinence than drugs that treat life-threatening diseases like malaria and HIV. This means there is a real profit stream from drugs the generics don't affect.

What protection exists to protect the rights of the drugs companies?
An agreement called TRIPS (Trade Related Intellectual Property Rights) introduced in 1994 by the World Trade Organisation protects patents on new drugs for 20 years, even in developing countries.

So does this mean generics are against the law?
Not necessarily against domestic laws. Laws relating to

patents and drug production vary from country to country and in many developing countries, such as India and South Africa, it is in the interest of the government to encourage the cheap flow of generics. This is reflected in the often-lax nature of national legislation surrounding generic production. Also, once a country's own generics companies become successful businesses, governments want to look after their interests. This can bring them into conflict with the foreign pharmaceutical companies.

In 2001 South Africa was sued by 41 pharmaceutical companies for their Medicines Act

How vigorously do pharmaceutical companies defend what they perceive as a breach of their rights?
Pharmaceuticals defend their drugs where they can, despite the fact that this can make them unpopular worldwide. For example, in March 2001 South Africa was sued by 41 pharmaceutical companies for their Medicines Act, allowing the importation and production of cheap generic Aids drugs.

The case was dropped after protests around the world. In 2007, the pharmaceutical Novartis began a challenge against Indian patent laws limiting the production of generics.

And the worldwide picture?
Fulfilling global public interest requires a balance between protecting intellectual property rights (to provide an incentive for research) on the one hand, and safeguarding public health by ensuring access to safe, effective medicines for all who need them on the other.

The **Doha Declaration**, adopted by WTO members in 2001, contains internationally agreed safeguards to ensure a balance between patents and public health in the light of the TRIPS agreement. It says the

"TRIPS agreement does not and should not prevent Members from taking measures to protect public health", enshrining principles the World Health Organisation has publicly advocated and put forward over the years. But these only have meaning if upheld.

THE ETHICS OF PANDEMICS MANAGEMENT – THE ISSUES

In the event of a pandemic, resources will have to be rationed.

Healthcare is increasingly a global issue. The African with TB who migrates to the developed world is not an 'African' problem.

Balancing the health needs of the global population with the benefits of free trade is an on-going area of debate.

PAST PANDEMICS – A CLOSER LOOK

The threat of a pandemic is nothing new. Killer diseases have been periodically wiping out sections of the worldwide population since time began, and even today we don't always have the answers to critical questions like; what caused them? And what made them disappear? The Black Death, Spanish Flu and smallpox are just three past pandemics. Pocket Issue takes a look.

THE BLACK DEATH

The Black Death, also known as the Plague, was one of the most lethal pandemics the world has ever seen. Beginning in central Asia, it spread to Europe by the mid 1300s and is estimated to have killed one fifth of Europe's population. Overall deaths resulting from the pandemic are estimated at 85 million. In England, for example, historians estimate that a pre-plague population of between 4 and 7 million collapsed to a post-plague figure as low as 2 million in the 1350s.

Did it only happen once?
No – the Black Death returned in almost every generation with varying deadliness. From the mid 14th century till the late 18th century, it returned in 100 epidemics.

Overall deaths resulting from the pandemic are estimated at 85 million

What caused the Black Death?
There is no absolute agreement on the cause of the Black Death. The most popular theory is that it was spread by rats. Scientists and historians have argued that it was spread by fleas, carried by animals such as the black rat (Rattus rattus). When rats died, the infected fleas found new hosts in humans and animals and infected them in turn.

55

Explanations of the plague's gradual disappearance vary. The most commonly accepted theory suggests that the black rat flea-bearing 'reservoir' for the disease was succeeded by the larger brown rat (Rattus norvegicus), which was not as prone as the black rat to transmitting the plague fleas. The interaction between this change, developing human immunity and rat ecology controlled the pattern of outbreaks, and the eventual and still mostly unexplained disappearance of the disease.

Contrary theories?

Recent research has questioned the belief that the Black Death was caused by bubonic plague. Graham Twigg, in his book The Black Death: A Biological Reappraisal, argues that due to the climate and ecology of Europe, it would have been almost impossible for rats and fleas to have transmitted the Plague.

However, like many of today's diseases, the Black Death was undoubtedly spread along sea and land routes by international flows of trade and labour.

Why was it called the Black Death?

Possibly because it caused victims to turn black due to haemorrhages under the skin. Alternatively it was a reference to the impact the disease had on everyone's mood when it was in circulation – bleak and miserable.

Overall deaths resulting from the pandemic are estimated at 85 million

What were the symptoms?

In the bubonic plague, the most common form during the Black Death, pustules appeared in the groin, the neck and the armpits, which oozed pus and blood. Skin and underlying tissue darkened as damage set in. Other symptoms included aching joints, vomiting and headaches.

Was there any treatment?

Nothing that proved effective. Four out of five people who contracted the bubonic plague were dead within eight days.

THE SPANISH FLU

The 1918 flu pandemic was an influenza pandemic caused by a strain of Influenza A – H1N1 – a subtype of influenza A, like bird flu. It lasted from 1918 to 1919. It spread across the globe, infecting 20% of the world's population. Normal flu infection rates are 0.1%. It is estimated that 50 to 100 million people died between 2.5 and 5% of the world's population. Which means it may have killed as many as the Black Death.

Spanish Flu deaths

Unit: number of recorded deaths

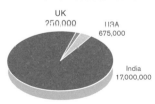

UK 250,000   USA 675,000

India 17,000,000

Source: Centers for Disease Control and Prevention

How did the disease progress?

The influenza struck hardest in summer and autumn, which was surprising given that common flu is usually worse in winter months. Within hours of being infected, healthy individuals could become incapacitated, dying the next day. The infection led to uncontrollable internal bleeding which flooded the lungs, turning the face blue. In some other patients, the flu led to a loss of bowel functions and death from the loss of vital intestinal lining. In the fastest progressing cases death resulted from pneumonia.

Why was it so deadly?

Research has suggested that the Spanish Flu killed using what is known as a 'cytokine storm' *(See page 28)*. This is a potentially fatal immune reaction, when the body's immune system has an exaggerated response to an infection and too many immune cells are activated. It is thought this most usually happens when the immune system is

57

facing a new and highly pathogenic infection such as Influenza A. Symptoms usually consist of high fever, swelling, redness and fatigue. Cytokine storms render a healthy immune system a liability.

It is estimated that 50 to 100 million people died

Which age groups suffered most from Spanish Flu?
While the very young and the elderly were affected, many victims were healthy adults, with strong immune systems capable of fighting off the common flu. Some 99% of the victims were under 65, and more than half were between 20 and 40 years old. The cytokine storm theory could explain why Spanish Flu death rates among young adults were so high.

Did the virulence of the flu have anything to do with World War I?
Spanish Flu was not caused by

the war, but the transport of vast numbers of troops in close quarters hastened its spread. And as with the Black Death and diseases today, the increased density of transport links facilitated the spread of the influenza.

Why was it called the Spanish Flu?
Although the disease was first observed in the US in 1918, the allies called it Spanish Flu because it was covered extensively in the Spanish press. As a neutral country, Spain had no wartime censorship.

How did the flu affect everyday life?
In many areas up to a third of the population was infected, meaning that the sheer number of people incapacitated brought the infrastructure supporting everyday life to a standstill. Shops closed for business, and healthcare workers were too ill themselves to treat the infected.

SMALLPOX

Smallpox is an acute contagious disease caused by the variola virus. Now completely eradicated from the world, it was one of the most devastating diseases known to mankind, with repeated epidemics cutting a swathe through populations around the globe for centuries.

How did the disease progress?

After an incubation period of 12 to 14 days, influenza like symptoms began, including fever, headache, back pain and sometimes vomiting. Next, the characteristic rash appeared, on the face and hands first, later progressing to the trunk of the body. Lesions grew into pustules, eventually scabbing and developing into scars in those who survived. Complications among survivors included blindness.

How deadly?

Some 30% of those infected were killed; while up to 80% of survivors were marked with deep-pitted scars, called pockmarks, most obviously on the face. As late as the 18th century, smallpox was killing every tenth child born in Sweden and France, and every seventh child born in Russia. The disease picked off rich and poor alike, counting Queen Mary II of England, Emperor Joseph I of Austria, King Louis XV of France and Tsar Peter II of Russia amongst its victims.

Treatment?

No effective treatment was ever developed for smallpox. The major breakthrough against the disease came with an early vaccine, arguably the first, demonstrated by Edward Jenner in 1798.

He inoculated patients with cowpox, a viral relation to smallpox, and this proved to confer immunity to smallpox as well. There was a risk sometimes the inoculated became very ill with a full-blown pox – but with the risks of smallpox being so much greater, generally it was hailed as a medical breakthrough.

> The World Health Assembly endorsed the global eradication of smallpox in 1980

How was smallpox eradicated?

In 1967, a global eradication campaign was launched by the WHO. At the time, smallpox still threatened 60% of the world's population. 1977 saw a single and last natural case, in Somalia. In 1978, there was a fatal laboratory-acquired case in the UK. The World Health Assembly endorsed the global eradication of smallpox in 1980.

Does this mean smallpox doesn't exist today?

Smallpox has effectively been eradicated, but it still exists under laboratory conditions. The WHO has voted against destroying the remaining samples, on the basis that they may be useful for development of future vaccines and treatments against disease.

So has the smallpox vaccine been discontinued?

No. Stocks still exist and are still held by many countries, but they are dwindling. Most usually, only those who come into contact with smallpox through their work are now vaccinated against the disease. Routine vaccination was discontinued following the eradication of the disease.

> Smallpox could be unleashed through war or bio terrorism

So, in theory, could smallpox make a comeback?

With the only known samples under laboratory lock and key, it's extremely unlikely. But the powers that be can't completely rule it out, so every now and then vaccine stocks are replenished. Ways it could be unleashed include through war or bio terrorism.

Dr Joshua Lederberg, a Nobel laureate in biology who advises the US on germ warfare, said:

"We have no idea what may have been retained, maliciously or inadvertently, in the laboratories of a hundred countries from the time that smallpox was a common disease. These would be the most likely sources of supply for possible bio terrorists".

PAST PANDEMICS – THE ISSUES

The Black Death was one of the most deadly pandemics the world has ever seen, and dominated for four hundred years from the 14th to 18th century before mysteriously fading away.

Spanish Influenza was a kind of avian flu, like bird flu. 50-100 million people died. The disease carried an infection rate of between 2 and 20% of the population.

Healthy adults with strong immune systems were just as vulnerable to the Spanish Flu as the more usual flu victims, the elderly and the young, suggesting a Cytokine Storm factor.

Global trade and labour routes flows helped the diseases to spread.

Smallpox, another deadly virus, was declared eradicated in 1980, but not before it had reaped 3,000 years worth of havoc across the world.

Despite smallpox's eradicated status, the experts seem reluctant to say it can 'never' return.

FUTURE PANDEMICS – POSSIBLE THREATS TO COME

So we've looked at past pandemics, and we've heard about the current threats, but what about the future? Are there any diseases out there with the potential to become future pandemics? Yes, lots. Including, most notably, Clostridium difficile. But other possibles include the Ebola virus and SARS. And are these influenced by other on-going changes, like global warming? Pocket Issue investigates.

CLOSTRIDIUM DIFFICILE (C. difficile)

This is a virulent strain of bacteria, first noted in 1978. It is carried harmlessly in the gut of half of children under two, but for people on long courses of antibiotics or with underlying illnesses, it can multiply within the intestine, producing toxins that damage the wall of the intestine and disrupt its normal function, leading to body fluids such as blood and water leaking into the intestine. This causes diarrhoea, which weakens the patient. C. difficile can also cause severe infections, ulcers, bleeding in the colon and perforation of the intestine.

How deadly?
Quite deadly. It is currently responsible for three times as many deaths as MRSA. It is not classified as a 'superbug' because it is not resistant to antibiotics but cases of C. difficile are becoming increasingly numerous. Case numbers have risen over the past 20 years from less than 1,000 in the early 1990s to 44,488 in 2004.

Poor hygiene can turn a couple of cases into a serious outbreak

Deaths?
The Healthcare Commission, an NHS watchdog, found that 1,100 patients at three hospitals in Kent, contracted the bug between April 2004 and September 2006. 345

62

patients died, 90 'definitely or probably' because of the infection. C. difficile was mentioned on 3,807 death certificates in England and Wales in 2005, rising to 6,480 citings in 2006, according to a study published by the Office of National Statistics.

How is it spread?
The spores of C. difficile are carried in the liquid faeces of the sufferer. Poor hygiene can turn a couple of cases into a serious outbreak.

Who is most at risk?
The elderly are a prime target. More than 80% of reported cases were in people over 65. Those in hospitals and nursing homes are also more likely to catch it, although infection with C. difficile in the community and outpatient setting is increasing. A late diagnosis and weakened immune system are key factors increasing a person's risk of death.

Why is it on the rise?
Once again, antibiotics and poor hygiene get the blame.

Broad-spectrum antibiotics knock out all other bacteria, giving C. difficile a chance to multiply in the intestine to the point at which they become dangerous. The disease is also resistant to some cleaning procedures. Bleach is needed to prevent its spread, and hands must be washed with soap and water.

> A vaccine is on the horizon, predicted to be ready for use by 2011

Is there a vaccine?
A vaccine is on the horizon, predicted to be ready for use by 2011.

What is the Government doing about C. difficile?
Surveillance for C. difficile is now compulsory in all hospitals. And the Health Act 2006, which brought a mandatory hygiene code to hospitals and care homes in England, should help.

Pandemic potential?
Could be knocked out if the vaccine under development proves effective. **One to watch**.

SARS

SARS, a new, highly contagious type of pneumonia, was identified in 2003. Over 8,000 people were infected, and 800 died. A virus, it didn't respond to antibiotics, and the world panicked that it was seeing the emergence of a new pandemic. However, local epidemics were halted before they could become pandemics.

Pandemic potential?
The last outbreak of SARS was controlled, and the global fear of a pandemic proved unfounded. However, it is possible SARS could re-emerge, so **complacency is not an option.**

EMERGING SUPERBUGS

MRSA is the most commonly known 'superbug' – a disease that becomes resistant to antibiotics – but other diseases are developing new antibiotic resistant strains. One such causing concern is TB. Superbugs can be controlled through good hygiene and clean hospitals, but to vulnerable people, those already ill, they can be deadly.

Pandemic potential?
Needs watching.

EBOLA VIRUS

This is a deadly virus, with the first cases occurring in 1976 in Sudan and Zaire. It is named after the Ebola River valley, which was the site of the first outbreaks. Scientists have speculated that both Ebola and SARS originated from bats.

Scientists have speculated that both Ebola and SARS originated from bats

How deadly is deadly?
Mortality is between 50 and 90%.

How is it transmitted?
Through direct contact with bodily fluids from an infected person.

What are the symptoms?
Symptoms include headaches, fatigue, nausea and abdominal pains, followed by diarrhoea, vomiting blood and pink eyes. The virus damages organs by perforating the capillary walls leading to massive haemorrhaging.

Could Ebola ever become contagious?
There is always a chance that diseases can mutate to become infectious without the need for close contact as with the bird flu threat and this would obviously increase the potential to become a pandemic.

Pandemic potential?
Currently limited by the fact that the virus struggles to spread via airborne transmission. However an infected person does live for an average of ten days, which means that the virus has plenty of time to infect others in the poor hospital conditions frequently found in the developing world. Avoiding needle sharing and better hygiene would reduce this risk. **One to watch.**

FUTURE PANDEMICS – THE ISSUES

C. difficile, a bacteria that already infects three times as many people as MRSA, must be taken seriously. A vaccine is under development and this could change the outlook if it proves effective and is in use by 2011, as currently predicted.

The Ebola virus, endemic in parts of the world, is not currently a real threat at present since it cannot spread through airborne transmission. However, if the germ should mutate to enable airborne transmission and germs do mutate the situation would be much more serious.

SARS scared the world when it first emerged, but proved to be containable. Next time?

DO WE NEED TO WORRY?

In terms of general pandemic risk, the UK is probably one of the safest places on the globe.

A human bird flu pandemic was recently declared a "low risk" by the UK Government, although the WHO says it's a case of not if but when. Plans are in place to protect the population if it does arrive. Millions have been invested in drugs to treat up to 14 million people.

Millions have been invested in drugs to treat up to 14 million people

MRSA and C. difficile are the key threats to the vulnerable in hospitals. However, hospitals are usually the last point of contact in the health chain. And measures, mostly based around cleaning, are ongoing in hospitals to try and reduce outbreaks and get these two bugs under control. A vaccine against C. difficile is also in the pipeline.

However, healthcare is a global issue. The conditions for potential pandemics to gain momentum exist in the developing world and could worsen should global warming continue as expected.

And the UK's connection to the developing world through trade, migration and tourism has never been stronger.

Worry factor: there's no point worrying about something you can't control. Check out our *What can you do?* section and then liberate yourself to concentrate on other things.

The Key Players

The people and institutions

THE KEY PLAYERS

Who are the organisations and people central to the prediction, management and treatment of a pandemic? Pocket Issue rounds them up.

THE WORLD HEALTH ORGANISATION (WHO)

What is it? The **WHO** is an agency of the United Nations, formed on 7 April 1948. The WHO has 193 member states. It is the co-ordinating authority for international health and succeeded the International Health Organisation (IHO), which was an agency of the UN's predecessor, the League of Nations.

What does it do?
The WHO has a constitution that states its objective as 'the attainment by all peoples of the highest possible level of health'. It does this by combating diseases, especially co-ordinating responses to major infectious diseases. It also supports the development and distribution of vaccines and drugs.

Where is it?
The central offices of the WHO are in Geneva and are staffed by 8,500 health experts and support staff. It has six regional offices in Republic of Congo, Denmark, India, Egypt, the Philippines and the USA.

Who is eligible for membership?
All UN member states. Other countries can be approved through a majority vote by the World Health Assembly, the representative body of the WHO.

Who funds the WHO?
Contributions come from member states and donors. These may be countries, but also might be non-governmental organisations, pharmaceutical companies and foundations such as the **Bill and Melinda Gates Foundation** and the **Rockefeller Foundation.**

Does it work with national healthcare systems?

Yes. It does many things on the level of individual nations, including providing and distributing information and research to countries, and maintaining a list of essential medicines that healthcare systems should make affordable to people.

How successful has it been?

Its biggest success was the eradication of smallpox in 1980, after years of health campaigning. Its attempt to eradicate polio has almost succeeded and it is developing a vaccine against malaria that would drastically reduce mortality in the developing world.

What work does it do to prevent new pandemics?

Taking the threat of bird flu as an example, the WHO has a network of 12 **National Influenza Centres** that monitors influenza activity. These will report signs of any "unusual" influenza virus to the WHO **Global**

Influenza Programme. "Rapid detection of unusual influenza outbreaks, isolation of possible pandemic viruses and immediate alert to the WHO system of national authorities is decisive for mounting a timely and efficient response to pandemics", says the WHO. The WHO has also drafted a Global Influenza Preparedness Plan.

Any problems?

Yes. Donor funders often want to control how their money is spent, which means that if they give enough, they can dictate the WHO's priorities. Donor governments are accountable to their voters and want to have some high profile successful results to speak of. Hence, for example, the US putting three fifths of its extra budgetary contributions into the global programme against Aids. It can make for a better headline.

What could be done to improve this?

Improved accountability and transparency within its central organisation would improve

71

trust from donor countries, and perhaps encourage them to return funding to the central organisation, rather than contributing to the special funding programmes which allow them to dictate where their money goes.

NON-GOVERNMENTAL ORGANISATIONS (NGOS)

What is an NGO?

NGOs are non-profit voluntary citizens groups, which can be organized on either a local, national or international level. NGOs perform a range of services and functions on areas ranging from human rights, health issues through to the environment. They are usually created by private people who play no part in government. International NGOs have been around since the mid-19th century, playing important roles in the anti-slavery movement and women's suffrage.

Accelerating globalisation in the 20th century increased the importance of the NGO as many problems could not be resolved within a single nation. It is estimated that there are 40,000 international NGOs operating around the globe.

What is their role in health provision?

NGOs operating in a healthcare area fulfil vital roles in both developed and developing countries. They can vary in their methods. Some act as lobbyists, while others will run programs of support or relief.

In developed countries?

In developed countries many NGOs exist to provide support to sufferers of chronic diseases such as cancer, HIV/Aids, diabetes and mental health illnesses. They provide networks of support and shared resources that less specialised national services cannot provide. A handful of examples include hospice providers like **Helen House** and mental illness charity **SANE**.

In developing countries?
NGOs in developing countries can play a huge part in plugging gaps that healthcare systems don't fill, as well as in bringing general relief and sometimes advocacy in a conflict situation. **Oxfam** is a well known international NGO concerned with alleviating poverty in developing countries. It runs many initiatives to this end, one being providing people with the equipment and skills to find food and clean drinking water. Another is Nobel Prize winner **Médecins Sans Frontières.** This is a humanitarian aid NGO known for its health work in war zones and developing countries with serious endemic disease problems.

A considerable organisation, each year around 3,000 doctors, nurses, midwives and logisticians are recruited to run projects, while around 1,000 permanently employed staff work to recruit volunteers and handle finances and media relations.

Are NGOs always independent from government?
NGOs can receive some funding from governments. Médecins Sans Frontières, for example, gets a portion of its funding from governments, as has Oxfam in the past. NGOs operating in healthcare will also need to work closely with government run national healthcare systems.

What would NGOs do in the event of a pandemic?
NGOs operating in developing countries deal with pandemics on an on-going basis, malaria and HIV/Aids being two examples. Governments and healthcare systems can and do keep relevant NGOs up to date on their national pandemic plans.

PHARMACEUTICAL COMPANIES

What do they do?
Pharmaceutical companies research, develop, market and distribute medicines.

73

What is their history?

Many of the existing pharmaceutical companies began life in the late 19th and early 20th centuries.

Switzerland, Germany and Italy led the way and the US and UK followed.

The current situation?

There are more than 200 major pharmaceuticals operating in one of the most profitable industries in the world. While areas of profit may change for example, advances in antibiotics have slowed and resistance to antibiotics may be increasing – pharmaceuticals look set to remain hugely profitable. Advances in biotechnology, as well as the human genome project, which will provide information about human DNA makeup, are two areas for continued growth.

What contribution do pharmaceutical companies make in the control of a pandemic?

Pharmaceutical companies manufacture the drugs and/or vaccines best known to fight a particular germ ear-marked as having possible pandemic potential, and research others that might fight a particular germ more effectively.

Why do pharmaceuticals come in for a lot of criticism?

Because while the profit motive is what drives pharmaceutical companies forward and this has undoubtedly led to the development of many life saving drugs, it does not always lead to the most useful outcome for customers and patients. Drug companies have been accused of 'over-medicalising' social and personal problems in order to create profit avenues. One example of this is Viagra.

How do Pharmaceuticals fund their drug research and development?

Drug companies defend their pricing by citing the need for profits to re-invest in research and development of new drugs. In other words, without present profits, the stream of future drugs dries up.

Do pharmaceuticals help the developing world?

Yes, up to a point. They are a critical source of medical aid for developing countries that often have a much greater burden of disease than developed countries. However, in the past pharmaceuticals have been accused of using the poor of developing countries in clinical trials without proper protection, consultation and care. For example, in 1996 a paediatric clinical trial conducted by Pfizer tested the antibiotic Trovan, apparently without obtaining the informed consent of participants or their parents.

There is also the issue of patents, for example for HIV/Aids medicine, keeping prices high and therefore limiting treatment options for patients in the developing world. But working on low-cost alternatives to expensive drugs to sell to the developing world is not in the interests of many pharmaceutical companies.

So are pharmaceutical companies 'bad'?

No. Large pharmaceuticals are a critical source of medical advancement. And with regulation, developing countries can benefit. Pharmaceuticals also engage in many charitable initiatives, although these do bring them PR benefits. For example, in 2006, Novartis spent US$755 million on initiatives worldwide, which improved access to medicines in the developing world, often through the donations of medicines to patients affected by leprosy, TB and malaria. They also offered support to humanitarian organisations with emergency medical needs.

GOVERNMENTS

Governments structure the types of healthcare available.

Primary care: basic medical treatment and non-hospital care. In the UK, this means GPs.

Hospital care: specialist care.

75

Public health: This includes preventative medicine such as screening, vaccination programmes and health education, as well as several other areas not immediately linked with conventional health services, such as housing, water supplies and food hygiene.

How are these ranked in terms of importance?
Public health is possibly the most important in terms of the health of a population. Primary care is the starting point for medical aid. Hospital care costs the most, has the highest status, and is the focus of most political attention.

What can governments do about pandemic control?
Most governments in the developed world have established a range of pandemic plans to control infection and protect the population in the event of a pandemic like bird flu. However, in a globalised world economy, where flows of labour and capital criss-cross national boundaries on a daily basis in a way individual nations cannot control, developing worldwide healthcare is vital. Boosting health systems for the underprivileged would be the surest way to prevent a global emergency.

How can this be done?
National governments could support transnational initiatives led by organisations such as the **European Centre for Disease Prevention and Control** (ECDC) and the WHO through further funding, while at the same time maintaining important relationships with these organisations.

THE EUROPEAN CENTRE FOR DISEASE PREVENTION AND CONTROL:

What is it?
The ECDC is an EU agency working to protect public health by providing information that enhances health policies formed by governments. It is a transnational agency that has

close ties with governing
bodies, but is independent
from national governments.

What role does it play?
It helps the EU fight infectious
diseases and other serious
health threats.

*And in the event of
a pandemic?*
It would run networks of
laboratories and operate an
early warning and response
system across Europe. It could,
for example, dispatch a team of
EU experts to investigate an
outbreak of bird flu that
appeared to have been
transmitted from human to
human in a European country.

Stargazing

What would be a good and bad scenario come 2020?

STARGAZING

Fighting a possible pandemic is a bit like waging a war against an invisible enemy. But the decisions we make today have consequences. Pocket Issue imagines what these might be, in terms of the good, the bad, and the terrible.

THE GOOD

Bird Flu: after several threatening outbreaks in rural areas of sub-Saharan Africa, the WHO reassesses its containment policy. Increased funding from WHO donors, who accept that the disease must be tackled on a global scale, enables them to work with existing health structures, taking medicines to those who need it. The WHO also strengthens its partnerships with NGOs and governments across the developing world.

These steps, coupled with the relative inefficiency of bird flu's transmission process, ensure that human-to-human transmission of bird flu remains a rare occurrence. Continued funding and monitoring also means any outbreaks are quickly contained and dealt with. Europe-wide, pandemic emergency plans are left to gather dust in back offices, a potential crisis averted.

The WTO relaxes its controversial trade rules, meaning drugs must be made widely available and affordable to developing countries, either through drug companies accepting cuts in prices or through the acceptance of the role generic drugs play in fighting disease.

Other diseases: Polio is fully eradicated by 2009. And by 2015, through the judicious use of DDT, more affordable impregnated mosquito nets and the development of an effective vaccine, malaria is much more controlled other than in very remote rural areas.
HIV/Aids: Building on the theme of global healthcare, more money is injected into

tackling this disease through better education and awareness in developing countries. Generic drugs bring hope of a prolonged life expectancy to the millions of sufferers in developing countries.

Overall, it seems that global equality in healthcare is becoming a realisable dream.

HEALTHCARE IN THE UK

MRSA: Gordon Brown's 'deep clean' initiative, cleaning each ward of every hospital in turn, gets off to a slow start but over time the number of MRSA cases starts to decline. This initial success is built on by the re-introduction of ward Matrons to supervise daily hygiene procedures in hospitals and care homes, and swift isolation of any identified cases prevents spread of infection. Routine MRSA tests, by a simple swab, are introduced on admission and discharge of patients. This also helps prevent the transmission of MRSA into the wider community.

Schools educate children about the importance of hygiene, teaching thorough hand washing as standard, to further reduce the spread of community MRSA. These measures limit the ability of C. difficile to thrive, making hospitals a safe place once again.

More generally, the impact of increased government spending begins to filter through to the patient. Several new hospitals are built, many with single patient rooms rather than wards, further reducing the chances of the spread of any infection. With health scares no longer in the headlines on a weekly basis, public trust in the NHS begins to return.

THE BAD

The developing world's public healthcare systems remain under funded and continue to fail their populations, with huge numbers of sub-Saharan Africans dying of preventable diseases. NGOs work within the constraints laid down by pharmaceutical companies and the WTO to produce generics wherever possible.

Bird flu: just one more disease for the developing world, most at risk through the habit of close contact with poultry and the lack of effective medicine, to contend with. The virus kills hundreds of thousands in Africa and some parts of Southeast Asia, but is always hampered by its inefficient human-to-human transmission.

AND THE TERRIBLE

Developing countries:
With pharmaceutical companies and the WTO standing in the way of freely available medicines to treat a large number of conditions, and the WHO lacking funds from donor countries, developing countries don't receive the aid they need.

Against a backdrop of political conflict, vast swathes of the African population die of potentially curable diseases including malaria, TB, HIV/Aids and the newest pandemic to sweep the globe, bird flu, which has mutated as feared to allow human-to-human transmission. Economies collapse, as communities are unable to cope with the burden on productivity from spiralling death rates.

Orphans fall on the welfare of overstretched aid agencies, and while a lucky few are airlifted to Hollywood to meet the growing trend for celebrity adoption, most languish in under funded, understaffed, overcrowded orphanages, all too often succumbing to easily preventable childhood diseases.

Europe and the US:

The outbreak of bird flu
spreads to the developed
world. Countries roll out their
pandemic plans, but healthcare
systems are quickly
overwhelmed. Emergency
quarantine measures curtail
global trade and travel, which
quickly leads to a shortage of
goods and services. Cities
descend into lawlessness, with
looting and burglary carried out
by the most opportunistic
citizens. It takes months for the
pandemic to begin to recede,
allowing for a return to some
semblance of normal life.

A national survey reveals that
every extended family has
lost at least two members to
the virus. Global warming
continues unchecked.
The worst effects are felt in
the developing world where
fresh water shortages have
encouraged diseases to spread
quickly through communities.
In the UK, malaria carrying
mosquitoes are now found in
the Thames Estuary and the
Norfolk Broads.

What can you do?

How you can make a mark

WHAT CAN YOU DO?

Our health and welfare is linked to both the conditions in our immediate environment and the wider world. But what can we do to improve the lot in each?

Think healthcare, think global

Giving money to an agency that provides aid to developing countries means you are doing your bit to take healthcare global. Examples include Médecins sans Frontières, who provide medical aid in crisis areas. They are one of the few international organisations providing health services in Mogadishu, Somalia, where political violence is a constant hazard. Oxfam is another.

First Step

Donate to an NGO. Visit Oxfam's website **www.oxfam.org.uk** or Médecins sans Frontières **www.msf.org** Want to take your charitable giving wider, but not sure how? **www.guidestar.org.uk** can help.

Look after yourself

Think Lady Macbeth, and wash your hands a lot, and certainly before eating. This nursery rule cannot be overemphasised.

Carry a handkerchief or tissue. If we all sneezed into something other than thin air (which is just air waiting for someone else to breathe in) a primary source of transmission for many germs would be foiled.

Look after skin wounds properly, however small they seem.

If you have to go into hospital: Keep clean. Take your own soap, a flannel, your own razor and moist hand wipes. Make sure your bed area is regularly cleaned. Report any unclean toilet or bathroom facilities to staff.

First Step

Be a hypochondriac: Keep up to date with the latest bird flu and other health news, at NHS direct: **www.nhsdirect.nhs.uk**

Make your voice heard

Write to your local MP to get the issue of global healthcare up the agenda or join or start a petition

to the Prime Minister.
First Step
Not sure who your MP is?
www.WriteToThem.com will
show you the way. Or visit the
Prime Minister's website,
http://petitions.pm.gov.uk

Watch what you eat

The global trade in food, for
example poultry, is one the main
routes for new diseases to reach
the UK. And it is also worth
noting that increased use of
antibiotics in intensively reared
animals could also limit the
effectiveness of some drugs in
combating human illnesses.
Think organic, free range, local.
Organic meat is free from
antibiotics and, if too pricey,
make sure you know where your
meats comes from and how it
has been reared – free range
livestock is generally less reliant
on antibiotics. Try and buy
seasonal, British food whenever
possible. Think twice about that
stop at the fried chicken joint
after a night in the pub.
First Step
Go to **www.meatmatters.co.uk**
to understand what the labelling
on meat really means. Find your

local farmers market at
www.farmersmarket.net or look
for local food in your
supermarket. Dig out or buy
a copy of *Pocket Issue, Food*
to discover what you are
really eating.

Cool it down

Global warming could have a
dramatic impact on the UK's
resistance to pandemics, both
through migration of people from
hard-hit developing countries
and the re-introduction of
diseases, such as malaria, as the
UK warms.

Everyone can make a difference,
from lightening their carbon
footprint to ensuring that our
politicians and businesses
commit themselves to greener
policies and practices.
First Step
See how you can cut down your
carbon emissions by visiting the
Energy Savings Trust,
www.est.org.uk/commit. Get
your hands on a copy of *Pocket
Issue, Global Warming* to learn
more about the subject and
how to lower your personal
carbon footprint.

Further Reading

The best places to keep up-to-date

FURTHER READING

Hopefully this Pocket Issue has given you a clearer idea of the issues surrounding pandemics and health in a globalised world. You can keep in touch with the issue through our blog:
http://blog.pocketissue.com

We don't presume to offer the last word on such a large topic so here are some useful reports, books and websites we sourced to research this guide – please use them as a starting point for your own further reading.

Keeping up-to-date

For general information about bird flu, the BBC website's special report, found on www.news.bbc.co.uk is useful, while The Guardian has a more rapidly updated feature at www.guardian.co.uk/birdflu

For more specialised information, go to the scientific journal Nature's site at http://www.nature.com/avianflu and the science magazine New Scientist at www.newscientist.com Both these publications are excellent for general public health issues as well.

Keeping safe

For reliable information about health issues that relate to you (including the pandemics discussed in this book), NHS Direct, www.nhsdirect.nhs.uk, should be your first port of call. Another useful resource is Patient UK at www.patient.co.uk

Policy-makers

To see how our government is planning to tackle bird flu, MRSA, and a multitude of other diseases, go to the websites of the Department of Health at www.dh.gov.uk and the Health Protection Agency, www.hpa.org.uk

For the EU perspective, head to the European Centre for Disease Prevention and Control at www.ecdc.europa.eu, and for a truly global viewpoint, head to the website of the Food and

Agriculture Organisation (a UN body) at www.fao.org

Your own research
If you have the stomach to dig deeper, the online encyclopaedia Wikipedia is always a good starting place for research. For public health in the UK, the Health Protection Agency website, www.hpa.org.uk, has many research documents to dig through. The British Medical Journal, publication of the British Medical Association, also provides many articles about domestic and international healthcare – see www.bmj.com For a more international approach, browse through the publications on the World Health Organisation website at www.who.int

For a decidedly critical take on the role of pharmaceutical companies in healthcare policy, head to the topic pages of the online magazine ZNet, at www.zcommunications.org

The Glossary

Jargon-free explanations

THE GLOSSARY
Jargon-free explanations for some key terms and organisations.

AIDS
Acquired Immunodeficiency Syndrome:
the most serious form of HIV.

Antibiotic resistance
The ability of a micro organism
to withstand the effects of
an antibiotic.

Avian Influenza Directive
An EU initiative that keeps
tight surveillance of bird flocks
and gives powers to restrict
animal movements.

Bird flu (or Avian influenza)
A contagious viral disease in animals
caused by a number of strains of the
Influenza A virus.

Black Death
Also known as the plague, one of the
most deadly pandemics of all time.

Bubonic plague
see Black Death.

Clostridium difficile
A virulent strain of bacteria first
noted in 1978.

Cytokine Storm
Cytokines activate the immune cells to
fight disease. If they activate too many
cells, a cytokine storm can result, with
fatal consequences.

DEFRA
Department for Environment, Food and
Rural Affairs, responsible for monitoring
birds for potential outbreaks of bird flu
in the UK. It has a bird flu helpline,
available at +44 (0) 8459 335577.

DoH
Department of Health. Responsible for
co-ordinating the pandemic response in
the UK.

Doha Declaration
2001 declaration from the World Trade
Organisation to attempt to ensure a fair
balance between patents and
public health.

Ebola Virus
A deadly virus, with the first cases
occurring in 1976 in Sudan and Zaire.
Named after the Ebola River valley,
which was the site of the first
outbreaks.

Endemic
A disease that is always present within
a population.

Epidemic
A widespread outbreak of disease
occurring in a single community or
geographical region.

ECDC
European Centre for Disease
Prevention and Control. An EU agency
working to protect public health by

providing information to governments that helps them improve their health policies.

Generics
Low-price copies of patented medicines produced by developing countries.

H5N1
The most lethal kind of bird flu.

HIV
Human Immunodeficiency Virus: a virus that attacks the cells of the immune system, which over time reduces the body's ability to defend itself against various illnesses.

HPA
Health Protection Agency (HPA), providing support to the DOH.

Malaria
An infectious disease carried by single cell parasites transmitted to humans via mosquitoes, who infect through their bite.

MRSA
Methicillin-resistant Staphylococcus aureus is a much more antibiotic resistant variation of the common bacteria Staphylococcus aureus, and causes hard to treat infections.

NGOs
Non-governmental organisations are non-profit voluntary groups that can perform a range of services or functions on areas ranging from aid relief

(e.g. Oxfam) to the environment (e.g. Greenpeace).

Pandemic
The emergence of a disease new to a population, which infects humans easily, causes serious illness and spreads rapidly.

Pathogenic
Causing disease, or capable of causing disease.

Phages
Viruses that invade bacterial cells and cause bacteria to destruct. Could be used to find MRSA.

SARS
A new highly contagious type of pneumonia identified in 2003.

Smallpox
An acute contagious disease caused by the variola virus, declared eradicated in 1980.

TRIPS agreement
Trade Related Intellectual Property Rights, introduced in 1994, protecting patents on new drugs for 20 years.

Tuberculosis (or TB)
A serious bacterial infection that mostly affects the lungs.

WHO
World Health Organisation. An agency of the United Nations, with 193 member states, it is the co-ordinating authority for international health.

95

Also from Pocket Issue

Gen up on the big global issues with these
essential titles from Pocket Issue... and sound
knowledgeable when others don't.

  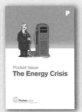  

"Precisely what's needed..."
Hephzibah Anderson, The Daily Mail

*"For everyone who longs to be well informed but lacks the time
(or the attention span)."* Alex Clark, The Observer

Now available in Audio – Order online at
www.**pocket***issue*.com

Pocket issue
Small briefs for a big world